Benjamin

Jubilate Deo in C

for SATB chorus and organ

CHESTER MUSIC

Published by

Chester Music
part of The Music Sales Group
14-15 Berners Street, London W1T 3LJ, UK

Exclusive Distributors:
Music Sales Limited
Distribution Centre, Newmarket Road,
Bury St Edmunds, Suffolk IP33 3YB, UK

Music Sales Corporation
180 Madison Avenue, 24th Floor,
New York NY 10016, USA

Music Sales Pty Limited
Units 3-4, 17 Willfox Street, Condell Park
NSW 2200, Australia

Order no. CH76560
ISBN: 978-1-84938-702-6
© 1961 by The Britten Estate Ltd
Worldwide publication rights licensed
to Chester Music Limited, 2009
All Rights Reserved

Cover design by Ruth Keating

Printed in the EU

www.musicsalesclassical.com

Written for St. George's Chapel, Windsor,
at the request of H.R.H. The Duke of Edinburgh

JUBILATE DEO

For Mixed Choir (SATB) and Organ

Benjamin Britten,
edited by David Willcocks

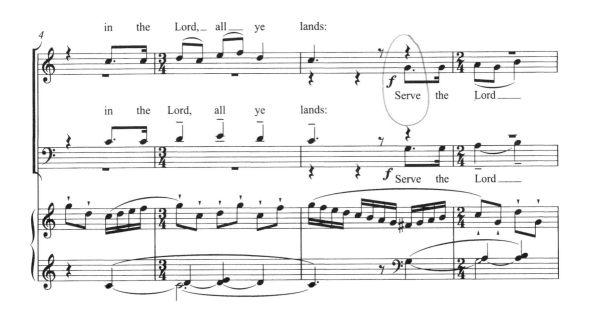

with glad - ness and come be-fore his pre-sence with a
with glad - ness and come be-fore his pre-sence with a

Be ye sure that the Lord he is
song.
Be ye sure that the Lord he is
song.

God:
it is he that hath made us and not
God:
it is he that hath made us and not

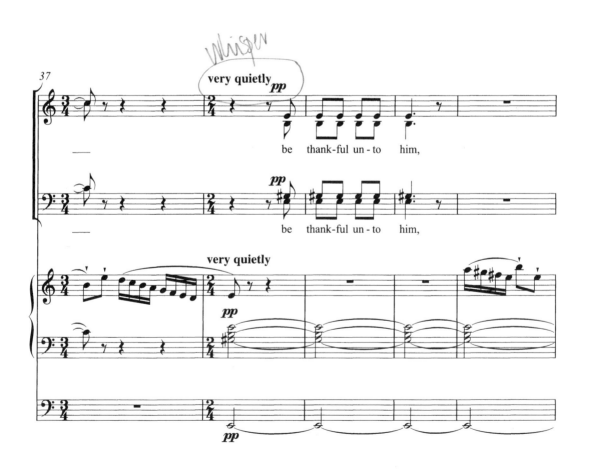

and speak good of his name.

and speak good of his name.

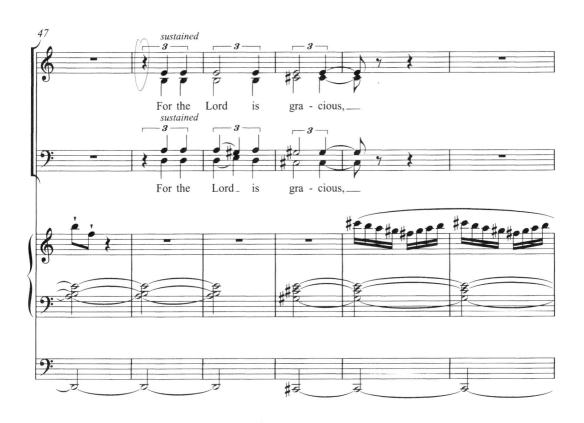

For the Lord is gra - cious,

For the Lord is gra - cious,

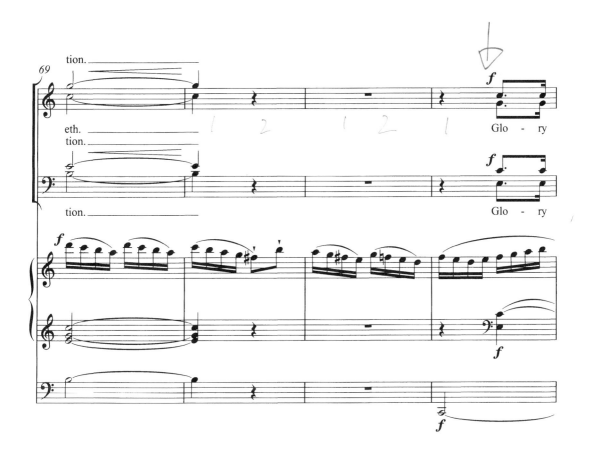

be _____ to the Fa - ther, and _ to _ the

be _____ to the Fa - ther, and to the

Son, and to _ the Ho - ly

Son, and to the Ho - ly

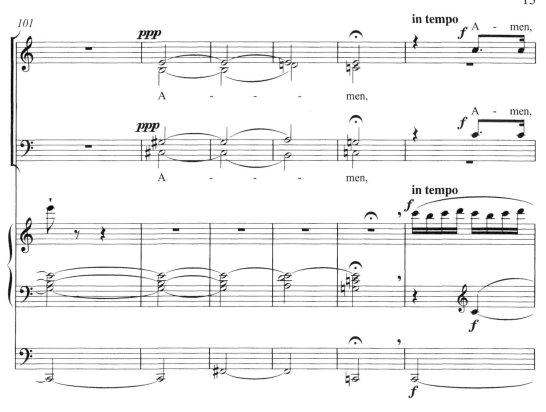

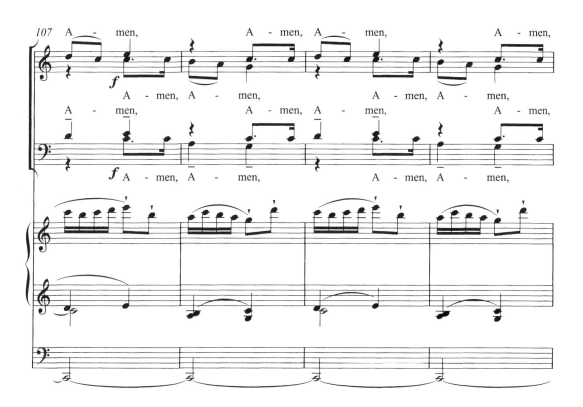

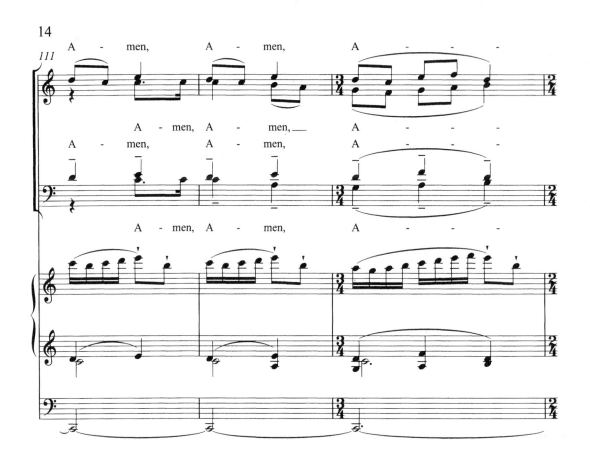

Aldeburgh, Feb. 1961